Feeling Beastly

Funny verse to read a

MARK BURGESS

Feeling Beastly

Illustrated by the author

MAMMOTH

For Rosemary

First published in Great Britain 1989
by Methuen Children's Books
Published 1990 by Mammoth
an imprint of Mandarin Paperbacks
Michelin House, 81 Fulham Road, London SW3 6RB
Reprinted 1990

Mandarin is an imprint of the Octopus Publishing Group

Text and illustrations copyright © 1989 Mark Burgess

ISBN 0 7497 0277 X

A CIP catalogue record for this title
is available from the British Library

Printed in Great Britain
by Cox & Wyman Ltd, Reading, Berkshire

Contents

The Wallaby

A wallaby, whenever it snows,
Suffers from a runny nose.
He keeps on sniffing to try and stop it
And has a hanky in his pocket.

Alphabestiary

A was an ass that didn't eat grass,
B was a beautiful bear,
C was a cat, incredibly fat,
And D was a dog with no hair.

E was an elephant, big as a bus,
F was a fidgety fox,
G was a goat, rowing a boat,
And H was a horse in a box.

I was an ibex high in the hills,
J was a jackal with 'flu,
K was a koala, asleep in the parlour,
And L was a louse upon you.

M was a mouse that lived in a house,
N was nothing-at-all,
O was an octopus that came to live with us
And P was a piglet (quite small).

Q was a quail, growing quite frail,
R was a rabbit that *walked*,
S was a snake that made a mistake
And T was the tiger it stalked.

U was an umbrella bird out in the rain,
V was a vegetarian vulture,
And W was a worm, trying to learn
About subterranean culture.

10

X was an oryx that stood on his head,
Y was a yak in the snow,
And Z was a zebra asleep in a bed,
Dreaming of what? — I don't know.

The Bat

The common flittermouse or bat
Lives inside a paper hat.
At night he flies about the sky
And makes an awful, creaky cry.

He paints his face with carpet glue
Because he likes to look at you,
And if your window he should pass
He'll stick his features to the glass.

Cats

Cats, it's a fact
That everyone knows,
Don't fall on their heads
But land on their toes.
So, why is it, then,
Whenever I'm there,
My cat's by the fire
With his *feet in the air?*

The Kangaroo

Once upon a time I knew
A happy, jolly, kangaroo.
He loved to joke,
He loved to laugh,
He loved to yodel
In the bath.

"Don't be sad,"
He'd say to me,
"Life's such fun
And smiling's free.
Buck up, be brave,
Be hale and hearty –
Come along and join the party!"

Oh, what merriment,
What delight.
We'd dance all day,
We'd dance all night.
The food we had
Was quite superb,
Better music
Never heard.
And when the time
Came round to go,
We'd thank him
For the jolly show.
He'd say, "So glad
That you could come.
Soon we'll have
Another one.
So hop along,
The lot of you,
Cheerio and
Toodle-oo!"

The Slumberglub

Nobody loves the slumberglub,
He's smelly and he stinks.
Nobody loves the slumberglub
(At least, that's what he thinks).
But he doesn't smell so awful –
His scent *delights* the nose.
The slumberglub is unaware
He smells just like a rose.

The Parrot

The parrot's a wonderful bird.
It can imitate speech, I have heard,
But mine will not talk,
Having said, with a squawk,
"Conversing with *you* is absurd."

Adam the Alligator

Adam the alligator,
Whenever he's home,
Talks for hours
On the telephone.
He dials the numbers
With a claw,
And talks from ten
'Til half-past four.
If you try to call *him*
the number's engaged
(So many's the time
I've been enraged).
And now, I've heard
Adam the alligator
Has got engaged
To the 'phone operator.

The Jigsaw Bird

I love to see the jigsaw bird
Flying upside down.
It sings a song that sounds all wrong
And wears a dressing-gown.

I love to see the sawjig bird
Flying downside up.
It feeds on chips and concrete mix
And drinks them from a cup.

Rodney the Rabbit

Rodney the rabbit
Has endless talents.
He's as strong as an ox,
He has excellent balance.

He can put up a shelf,
He can paper a wall,
He can solve any problem
In no time at all.

He can do his own cooking,
He can launder his clothes,
Whatever the question,
The answer he knows.

For Rodney the rabbit
Is terribly clever,
As he'll happily tell you
for ever and ever.

The Wasp

The humble wasp is much maligned,
He really is extremely kind.
Any chap in striped pyjamas
Couldn't really mean to harm us.
It's just he thinks he's still in bed,
Mistakes his tail for his head –
And doesn't mean to use his sting
But only kiss us, silly thing.

Mr and Mrs Fernsey-Howes

Mr and Mrs Fernsey-Howes
Often had domestic rows.
They called each other names and swore.
They wrestled on the kitchen floor.
They tossed the pans, they chucked the china,
The damage done was never minor.
The noise they made was simply frightful.
I never heard of two so spiteful.

That was until one fine Spring day,
For then a tiger came to stay.
He walked up the path, he rang the bell
And (just in case) he knocked as well.
"What do you want?" said Mrs F.
And then she gasped, she caught her breath.
The tiger whispered in her ear:
"Bring in my trunk, now, there's a dear."

And then he went straight in to where
Mr F. sat in his chair.
"Now listen," said the earnest cat,
"I make the rules and that is that.
Breakfast at eight, lunch at one,
I like my omelettes under-done."
And when the tiger this had said,
He left the room and went to bed.

No longer do the Fernsey-Howes
Rant and have domestic rows.
No more the sound of kitchen riot;
Their house is peaceful, utter quiet.
The tiger is the perfect gent,
The neighbours think him heaven-sent,
Respected everywhere he goes —
Perhaps he'll soon be mayor, who knows?

The Flamingo

With flamingos, it's not as you'd think –
They're not really meant to be pink.
The Almighty thought blue,
An appropriate hue,
But knocked over his bottle of ink.

Armadillo

An armadillo
When illo
Eats his fillo
And then sleeps
With his head
On a pillow.

Jungle Joke

There's a joke about
That would make you shout –
The piglet giggled at it,
The tamarin grinned,
The crocodile smiled,
The giraffe laughed,
The jackal cackled,
The jackdaw guffawed,
And as for the hyena –
Well, you should have seen her.

The Dinosaurs

The dinosaurs have come to town,
They've come to do their shopping.
They're thrilled to bits – tea at The Ritz
And then they're going bopping.

The Brontosaurus needs a hat,
Triceratops, a coat.
Tyrannos' Rex will sign the cheques
(The rest of them are broke).

The Stegosaurus orders buns,
Diplodocus, currant cake.
The Trachodon bops on and on
And gets a tummy ache.

The dinosaurs are going home,
Their shopping's all been done.
"We had a ball," say one and all,
"Extinction – here we come!"

Rats

To be a rat must be such fun,
I often wish that I was one.
Rats don't have to wash their hands,
They run around in happy bands.
They dance in mud, they play with goo,
No one tells them what to do.
And rats don't have to be polite
Or even go to bed at night!
But life is risky for the rat . . .

. . . Perhaps I'd rather be a *CAT*.

The Crocodile Next Door

A crocodile lives next door,
He's scaly and he's green.
He is the biggest crocodile
That I have ever seen.

He's fierce and terrible that croc',
He has a ghastly grin.
He'll gnash his teeth and likes to think
That you're afraid of him.

But don't be afraid, the horrid beast
Won't think of eating *you*.
Oh, the most disgusting things
Are what he likes to chew.

And he has an awful secret
(Poor beast, it pains him so),
His teeth are only DENTURES.
I'm his dentist – I should know.

Miranda

A girl called Miranda
Sent for a panda.
There arrived at the gate
Not one box but *eight*.
And when she opened them,
What pandamonium!

The Spotted Cow

While walking down a country lane
I met a spotted cow.
The cow, she curtsied daintly,
I answered with a bow.
I doffed my cap, I raised my voice:
"Dear cow, how do you do?"
The cow, she stopped her chewing
And said quite simply, "Moo."

Roberta Hyde

The trouble with Roberta Hyde
Was she was never satisfied.
She'd criticize the whole day long,
Everything was always *WRONG*.
"I don't like this. I don't like that.
I don't want a dog – I want a cat.
This pudding's cold, I want it hot.
I want the things I haven't got!"
Her suff'ring parents meekly tried
To keep their offspring satisfied,
A task that was gargantuan –
It just went on and on and on.

One day into the countryside
The family went for a ride.
They'd packed the car with things to eat –
Buttered scones and luncheon meat –
And when a pretty spot they found
They spread the picnic on the ground.
Roberta (who was always rude)
Said, "Shan't eat *that* – it's horrid food."
Her parents with a weary sigh
Didn't ask the reason why,
But said instead, "Don't wander, dear,
The woods are wild, so stay right here."
Roberta, though, was never good
And wandered off into the wood.

37

Alas, by chance, she passed the lair
Of a large and hungry bear.
The beast (he didn't mean to hurt her)
Stuck out a paw and grabbed Roberta.
His mouth, he opened very wide
And popped the little girl inside.
Later on, he told his chums,
"The infant really wasn't yums –
Hardly sweet, a trifle tough
And there wasn't quite enough."

The Literary Lions

The literary lions assemble each month
For a splendid, wonderful, literary lunch.
And what are they given to stop them being boring?
And what are they given to stop them from snoring?
Why, those literary lions are given for luncheon
Celery, cheese and cream crackers to crunch on.

The Impresario

A walrus lived in ice and snow
Who was an impresario.
Each summer, in the month of June,
He'd get an orchestra to tune.
Seals, sat on icy floes,
Played violins and piccolos.
Whales blew the bass trombones
And reindeer played the saxophones.
The conductor was a polar bear
(He waved his baton in the air)
And birds and beasts from miles around
Came along to hear the sound.
The concerts were so well-attended
All were sorry when they ended.
And close to where the music played
A painted notice was displayed:

AUDIENCE APPLAUSE IS NICE
PLEASE, NOT TOO LOUD –
YOU'LL CRACK THE ICE.

Jim the Hippopotamus

There once was a hippo called Jim
Who was terribly terribly *thin*.
For whatever he ate
To add to his weight
It made no difference to him.

"Try bananas – they're fattening things,"
Said a bird with beautiful wings.
So Jim ate for lunch
Bunch after bunch
Of bananas, including the skins.

But still Jim is not at all fat
Though he's no longer sad about that,
For he swings through the trees
And with elegant ease
Drops in on his friends for a chat.

Teacher's Pets

Terence is slow as a garden snail,
Pete is as strong as a lion,
William Smith is wise as an owl,
And a wonderful cheetah is Brian.

The Fly

Why, oh why,
Did the housefly fly?
To be sure
It was the spider spied her.
But he caught her in his web
And bashed her on the head
And in his frying pan fried her.

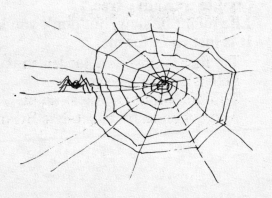

The Sloth, That's Me

I love to do just nothing,
Just nothing, all day long.
I'm lazy, very lazy,
But I ask you, what's so wrong?

The world it whizzes by outside
At a fast and dizzy pace.
What is the point, please tell me
Of that busybody race?

I love to do just nothing,
To hang about the trees,
To twiddle my toes or have a doze
And live a life of ease.

I haven't any worries,
My life is trouble-free.
Life might be slow, but don't you know
It is just *right* for me.

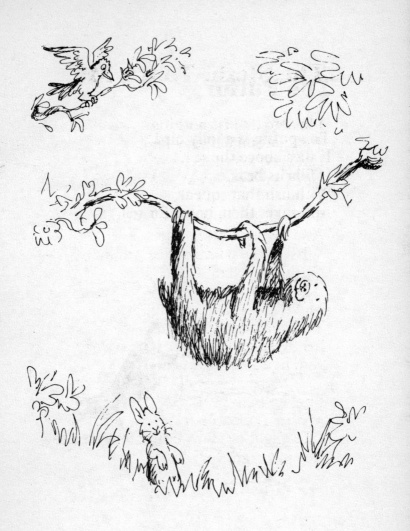

The Puffin

The puffin is a jolly bird,
It flies above the sea.
It fills its beak
With fish that squeak
And takes them home for tea.

Regina

I once met a pretty hyena,
Known by the name of Regina.
Each day she would dance
When she got the chance
And now she's a top ballerina.

Danny

Our dog Danny
Is off his food.
His dinner's untouched,
His bone's unchewed.
He doesn't want his biscuits,
He doesn't want his meat,
He doesn't want anything
Dogs usually eat.

But I think I know
(From the twinkle in his eye)
What our dog Danny
Would really like to try:
He knows what's for lunch,
He knows what's cooking —
He'd *really* like roast beef
And chocolate pudding.

Hen and Pig

A hen and a pig went for their hols
Riding in a hired Rolls.
About the countryside they drove
From Ditchling Beacon down to Hove
And then along to Beachy Head –
"Gosh, what a view!" the piggy said.
"But I think I'd better put the brake on
Or we'll end up as eggs and bacon."

Fred the Fly

Fred was a fly
Who was frightfully clever.
He could tell you the time,
He could forecast the weather.

He had read lots of books
From cover to cover
And he knew lots and lots
About something-or-other.

But the one thing Fred
Just couldn't have spotted
Was me with the paper
Before he was swotted.

The Toad

The toad is given to reflection
On the state of his complexion.
For this he is extremely fond
Of gazing often in the pond.
The creature is immensely vain
And even sits there in the rain.
And if he's feeling out of sorts
He cheers himself by counting warts.

The Ocelot

The ocelot
Has lots of spots,
He's a master of disguise.
He likes to wear dark glasses,
Waistcoats and bow ties.
He has read a lot of books
(Both little ones and large)
On Blending into Backgrounds
And the Art of Camouflage.
So he walks about the jungle
With his bow tie neatly knotted
And that clever ocelot
Is never ever spotted.

The Herring and the Whale

"How long is your tail?"
Said the herring to the whale.
"If I tell you," said the whale,
"You will laugh.
For my tale goes from me
To the Caspian Sea
And takes an hour and a half."

"Good gracious," said the fish,
"That's as long as I could wish,
I really haven't time
For any more.
You see, I have to dine
With a certain friend of mine
And it's very nearly half-past four."

"But we could go tomorrow,"
Said the whale with a swallow.
"You could travel on the tip
Of my fin.
Then you could tell your friends
You've visited both ends
And many other places in between."

The Slug

The slug he is so greedy,
He is no friend of mine.
He lives among my lettuces
On which he likes to dine.

When he's finished every one
And left a trail of slime,
He'll start upon the radishes
And eat them, one at a time.

He'll eat anything, that slug,
He thinks that that's just fine,
And, perhaps, if he's *still* hungry —
He'll even eat this rh-

Polly

Polly, while walking in the jungle,
Made a really serious bungle.
She sat right down upon a snake
And didn't realise her mistake.
All at once she felt the trees
(As it were) begin to squeeze –
A horrid, green boa constrictor,
The funny thing, it only licked her.

The Penguin

The penguin lives in Southern Seas,
He likes the colder climes.
His favourite dish
Is battered fish
With chips, wrapped in The Times.

Feeling Beastly

I'm really feeling beastly,
It's a beastly sort of day.
Everything is beastly
In a beastly sort of way.

The crododile is crying again,
It's raining cats and dogs,
The house is full of elephants,
The mice are wearing clogs.

There's a cockroach in the kitchen,
There's a spider in the bath,
There's a blockage up the chimney –
It's a forty-foot giraffe.

The horse has gone and bolted,
But left the door ajar,
And the silly geese have taken flight
In my motor car.

The bats aren't in the belfry,
The cows are all forlorn,
And the mole has made a mountain
In the middle of the lawn.

The bally ducks are grousing,
The frogs are hopping mad,
There's something fishy going on
Beneath a lily pad.

And I'd better count the chickens
For they're hatching from their shells.
It'll take a month of Sundays
And a week of wishing wells.

But I'll have to grin and bear it
And I'll find some beastly way,
And anyhow tomorrow
Is another beastly day.